Sawan

ENGLISH
WRITING BOOK
CAPITAL LETTERS

Name : AATHIR R

Class : A   Roll No. ....

Sec. : ....

School : ....

MANOJ PUBLICATIONS

A

FOR **AEROPLANE**

SAY, TRACE AND WRITE

A	A	A	A	A	A	A	A	A	A

A	A	A	A	A					

A	A	A							

A	A								

A									

A									

A									

A									

A	A	A	A	A	A	A	A	A

ANT

APPLE

AXE

FOR **BIRD**

SAY, TRACE AND WRITE

B B B B B B B B B B

B B B B

B B B

B B

B

B

B

B

B B B B B B B B B B

B

B

B

B

B

B

B

B

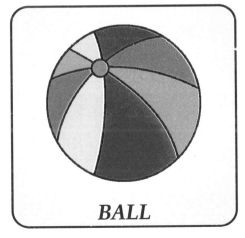

BALL

BUTTERFLY

BANANAS

Date : ....

5

Teacher's Signature : ....

C

FOR COW

SAY, TRACE AND WRITE

C C C C C C C C C C

C C C C

C C C

C C

C

C

C

C

CAR

CAT

CAKE

FOR **DUCK**

SAY, TRACE AND WRITE

D D D D D D D D D D

D D D D

D D D

D D

D

D

D

D

Date :   8   Teacher's Signature : ....

D D D D D D D D D D D

D

D

D

D

D

D

D

D

DOG

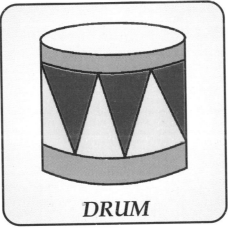

DRUM

DEER

Date : ....

Teacher's Signature : ....

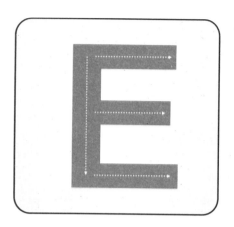

FOR **EAGLE**

SAY, TRACE AND WRITE

E E E E E E E E E E

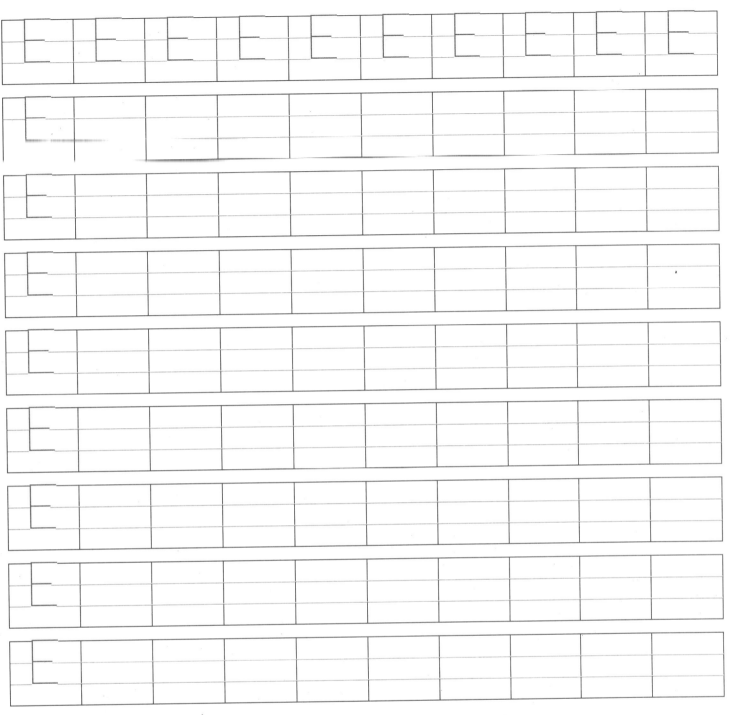

ELEPHANT

ENGINE

EGGS

Date : ....

Teacher's Signature : ....

FOR **FLAG**

SAY, TRACE AND WRITE

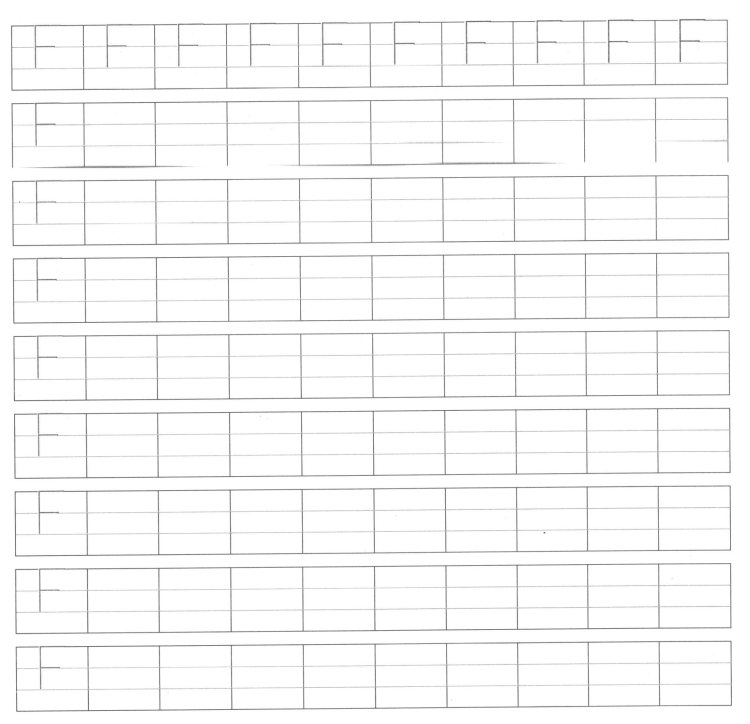

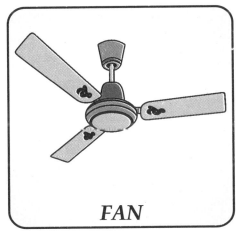

FAN

FLOWERS

FISH

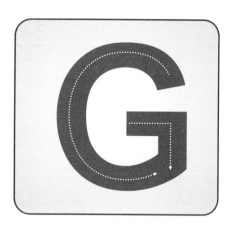

FOR **GOAT**

SAY, TRACE AND WRITE

G G G G G G G G G G

G G G G

G G G

G G

G

G

G

G

G G G G G G G G G G

G

G

G

G

G

G

G

G

GUITAR

GRAPES

GLASS

Date : ....

Teacher's Signature : ....

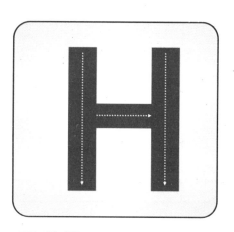

FOR **HOUSE**

SAY, TRACE AND WRITE

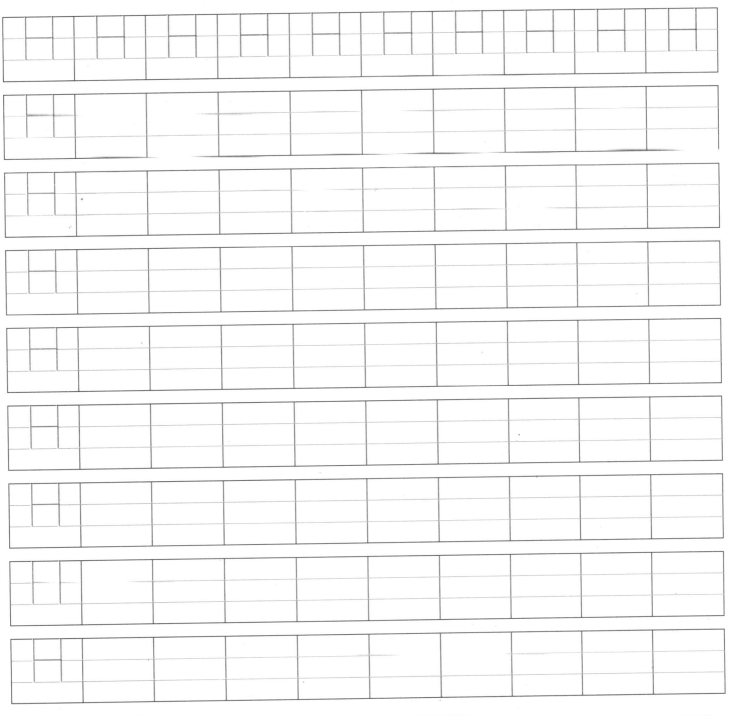

HELICOPTER

HORSE

HAT

Date : ....

Teacher's Signature : ....

FOR **INKPOT**

SAY, TRACE AND WRITE

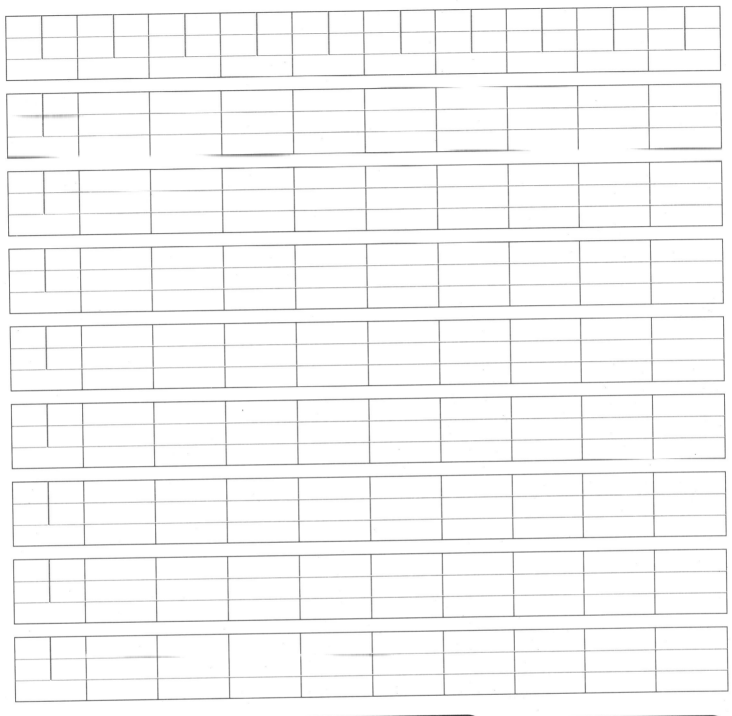

IRON

ICE CREAM

IGLOO

Date : ....

Teacher's Signature : ....

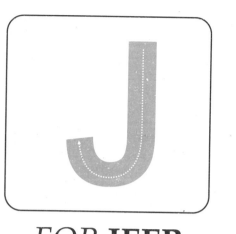

FOR **JEEP**

SAY, TRACE AND WRITE

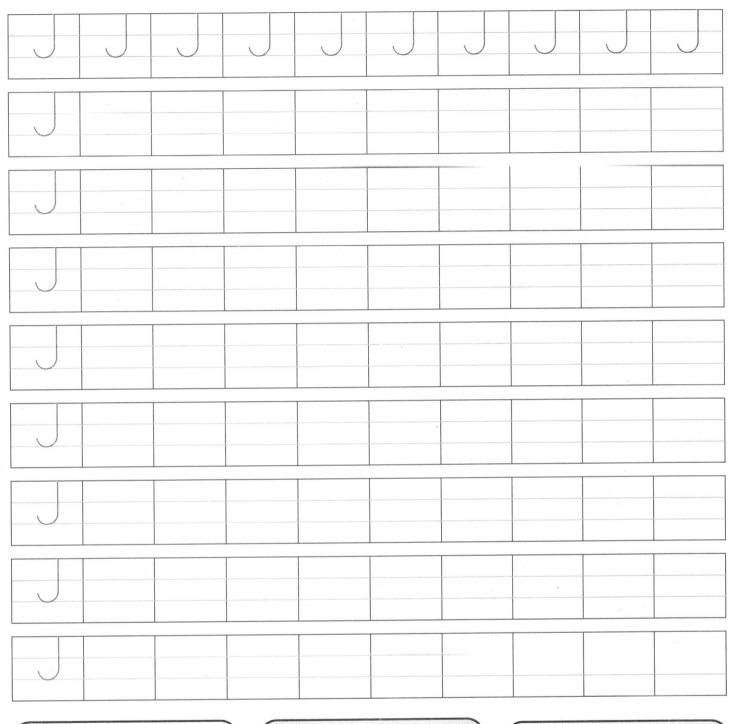

JOKER

JUG

JAM

Date : ....

Teacher's Signature : ....

FOR **KOALA**

SAY, TRACE AND WRITE

K K K K K K K K K K K

K K K K K

K K K

K K

K

K

K

K

K K K K K K K K K K K

K

K

K

K

K

K

K

K

KITE   *KANGAROO*   *KEY*

Date :   23   Teacher's Signature : ....

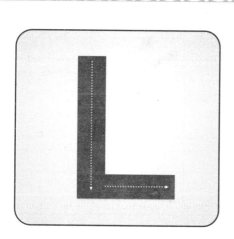

FOR **LION**

SAY, TRACE AND WRITE

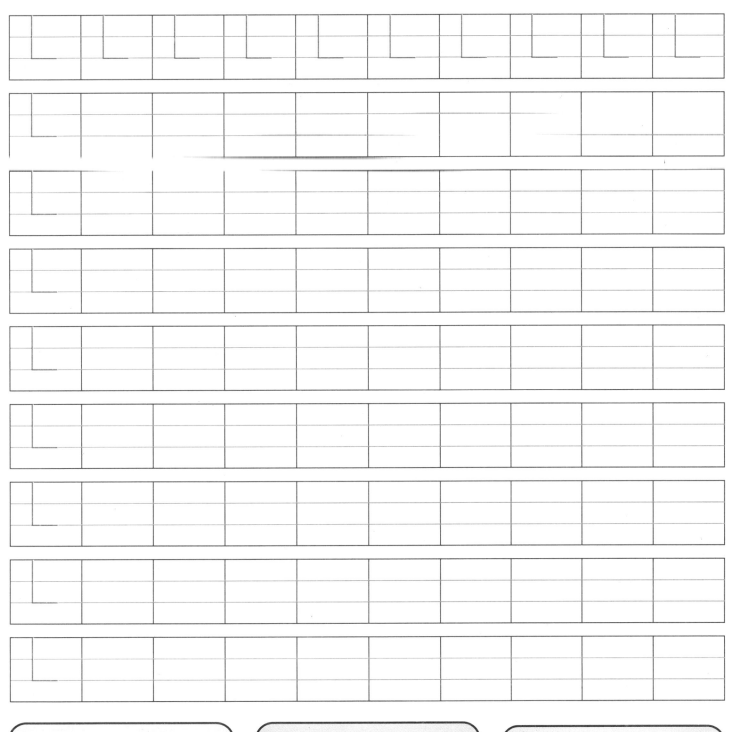

LOCK

LAMP

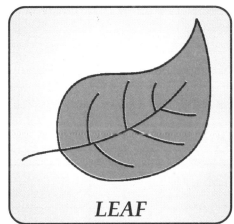

LEAF

Date : ....

25

Teacher's Signature : ....

FOR **MONGOOSE**

SAY, TRACE AND WRITE

M M M M M M M M M M M

M M M M

M M M

M M

M

M

M

M

M M M M M M M M M M

M

M

M

M

M

M

M

M

MANGO

MASK

MONKEY

Date : ....   Teacher's Signature : ....

FOR **NEST**

SAY, TRACE AND WRITE

N N N N N N N N N N

N N N N N

N N N

N N

N

N

N

N

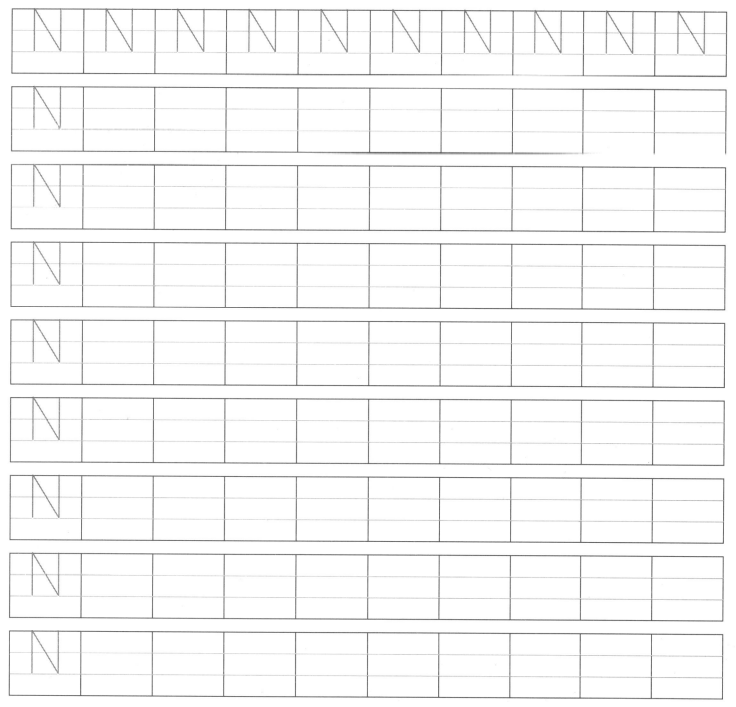

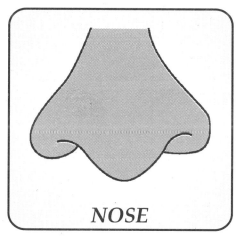

NOSE

NIB

NECKLACE

Date :   Teacher's Signature : ....

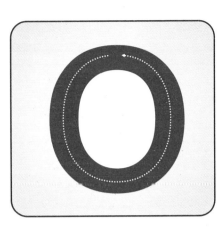

FOR OSTRICH

SAY, TRACE AND WRITE

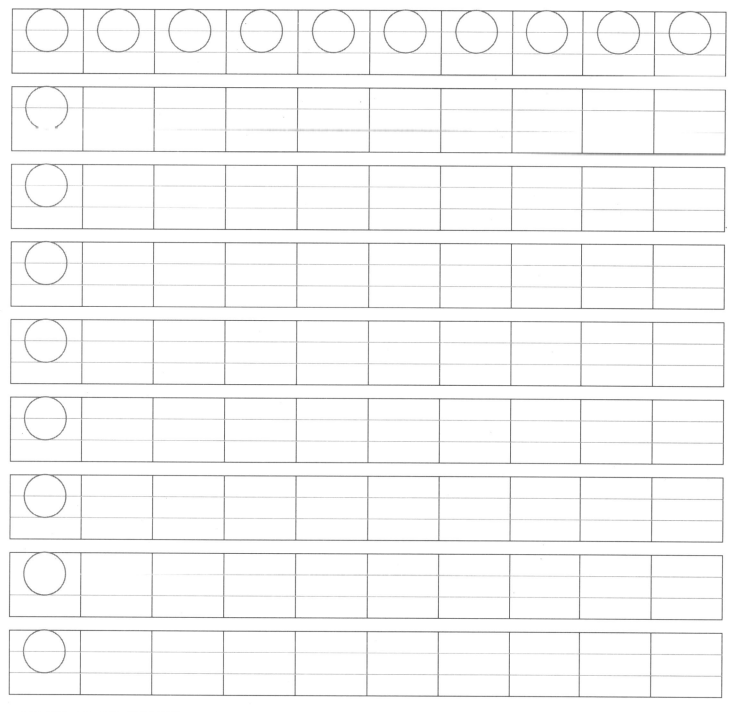

OWL

OCTOPUS

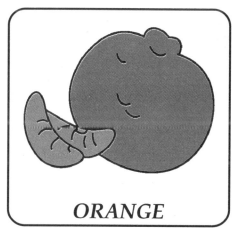

ORANGE

FOR **PEAR**

SAY, TRACE AND WRITE

P P P P P P P P P P P

P P P P

P P P

P P

P

P

P

P

English Writing Book Capital Letters

P P P P P P P P P P P

P

P

P

P

P

P

P

P

PAPAYA   **PARROT**   **PEACOCK**

Date : ....   Teacher's Signature : ....

FOR **QUEEN**

SAY, TRACE AND WRITE

Q Q Q Q Q Q Q Q Q Q

Q Q Q Q

Q Q Q

Q Q

Q

Q

Q

Q

QUILT

QUAIL

QUILL

Date : ....

35

Teacher's Signature : ....

FOR **REINDEER**

SAY, TRACE AND WRITE

R R R R R R R R R R

R R R R R

R R R

R R

R

R

R

R

R R R R R R R R R R R R

R

R

R

R

R

R

R

R

ROSE

RABBIT

ROCKET

Date : ....

37

Teacher's Signature : ....

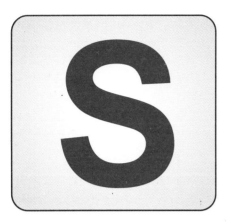

FOR **SWAN**

SAY, TRACE AND WRITE

S S S S S S S S S S

S S S S

S S S

S S

S

S

S

S

T

FOR TRUCK

SAY, TRACE AND WRITE

U

FOR UMBRELLA

SAY, TRACE AND WRITE

English Writing Book Capital Letters

FOR **VULTURE**

SAY, TRACE AND WRITE

Date : ....

Teacher's Signature : ....

FOR **WATERMELON**

SAY, TRACE AND WRITE

W W W W W W W W W W

W W W W W

W W W

W W

W

W

W

W

FOR XMAS TREE

SAY, TRACE AND WRITE

Date : ....

Teacher's Signature : ....

FOR **YAK**

SAY, TRACE AND WRITE

Z
FOR ZEBRA

SAY, TRACE AND WRITE

Z Z Z Z Z Z Z Z Z Z Z Z

Z Z Z Z

Z Z Z

Z Z

Z

Z

Z

Z

Date : ....

45

Teacher's Signature : ....

CONNECT THE OBJECTS WITH ALPHABET THEY START WITH

D
H
V
A
C
S
Y
R

WRITE THE FIRST ALPHABET OF THE OBJECTS IN THE BOX

Date : ....

Teacher's Signature : ....

ENCIRCLE THE ALPHABET THE PICTURES START WITH

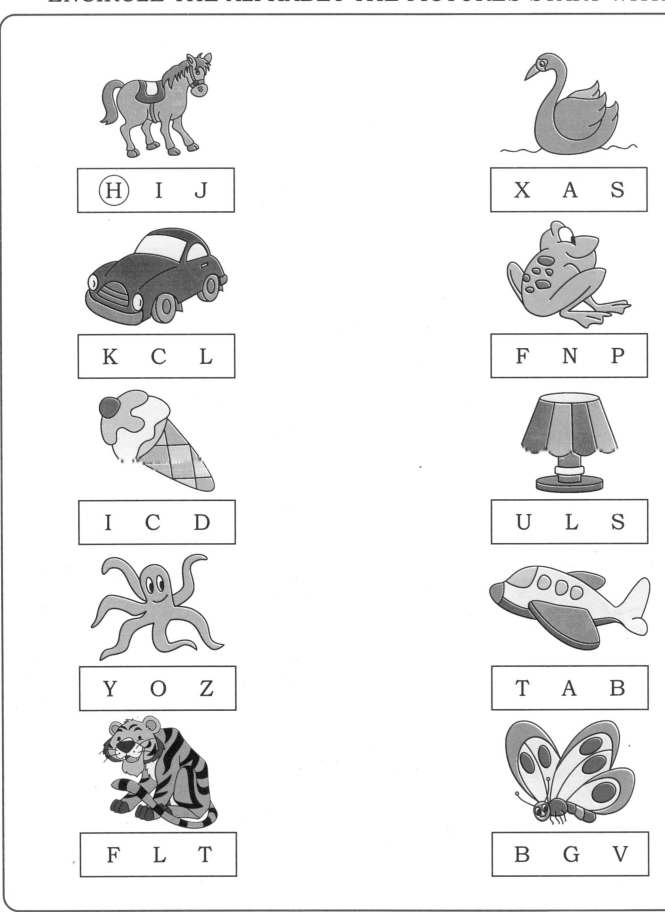

(H) I J

X A S

K C L

F N P

I C D

U L S

Y O Z

T A B

F L T

B G V

Date : ....

Teacher's Signature : ....